TEXTUAL NOTES

Composition first two movements, Vienna, 3 January 1788
(according to Mozart's catalogue); third
movement, Vienna, 10 June 1786, revised
?end 1787–beginning of 1788

Sources first edition, *Sonate pour le forte-piano, ou clavecin
composé par Mr W.A. Mozart* (Vienna:
Hoffmeister, 1788)[E]; autograph lost, except
earlier version of third movement, in the
collection of Felix Salzer, New York, reproduced
in *The Music Forum*, i (1967), 6–8 [A]

Notes The finale of this sonata was composed, in 1786,
as an independent rondo; it was published
separately in its original form by Birchall &
Andrews, London, as no.4 of vol.i of *Storace's
Collection of Original Harpsichord Music*, on 26 April
1788, and in the same year (probably later) by
Bossler, Speyer. Mozart composed the first two
movements by 3 January 1788; in view of the
fact that the three movements were immediately
published as a sonata, it is reasonable to suppose
that Mozart wrote the new ones specifically to
make up the complete work, and revised the
rondo to fit it as a finale to them. His main change
was the addition of a 'cadenza', bb.143–69, to
lend the movement extra weight apt to its role
as a finale, and to change the tempo from
Andante to Allegretto. Since Mozart revised the
movement, the later source is clearly the more
important; but the discrepancies are many, and
the engraving of the edition is careless, so we
print below a full list of points where the texts
differ. E shows all turns with a vertical stroke;
comparison with A in the rondo shows that a
normal turn is intended. The RH in A is notated
in the soprano clef.

1st movt
bar
16   RH slur 2–5
39   RH 1 e''' in most edns, but c''' in E
          (analogy with 167 is false as different harmony)
49–50   *sf* marks here but not at analogous points; *f* added
          by analogy
80–81   RH slurs ambiguous, probably 80, 1–3, 4–6; 81,
          1–4, 5–8; cf. 213ff
167   some edns give LH 3 d♭, but source as shown
195,199   slurs to 1st note of next bar (cf. 68, 72)
213–8   RH slurs ambiguous: tie 212–3 missing, slurs
          probably 213, 1–3, 4–7; 214, 1–4, 4–7; 215–8,
          all 1–3, 5–7 (214, 4 stacc.)

2nd movt many of the long RH slurs ambiguous, for example
          in 34f, 48f, 102f
bar
35   LH apparently tie/slur 3–9, presumably misprint
36   RH slur ?begins on 3
44   RH slur begins on 2: cf. 42
58   LH 10 stacc.
69   RH 5 ♮
70   RH 3 ♭
94   LH slurs 1–7, 8–11 (?because of clef change)
112   tie and slur contracted into one by engraver:
          cf. 42, 44, 110
113   RH 1st slur begins on 4
116   LH slur ?to 2nd beat; RH 3rd slur ?5–6 only

3rd movt A has tempo marki
bar
1   *p* not in A or E, bι
          catalogue; A lacks
1–3   LH, A and E 1 slur per bar; cf.7 and 9 (all 1 slur
          in A and E) and 39ff etc.
5   RH slur not in A
7   see 1
11   RH stacc. not in A (cf. 49)
17,20   A stacc. dots, not wedges
18   RH 5–7 slur and stacc. not in A
22   RH slur not in A, in E ?1–9, but cf. 135
24   LH slur not in A
25   RH slur and stacc. not in A
26   RH slur not in E
27–8   E, LH slurs lacking; A, RH slurs 27, 5–6, 28, 5–10
29   RH, 1st and 2nd slurs not in A
30–33   A, no LH slurs
34–5   E, RH slur to 34, 12 only
36–7   A, RH slur to 36, 12, E to 37, 2; A, no articulation
          in 37
38   A, RH, no stacc. on 6
39   A and E, RH slur 1–5 only: cf. 45, where slur in
          A and E is to a''
39–47   LH slurs: A, 39–40 and probably on to 41 (new
          system), 45–7; E, 39–40, 41, 45–6, 47
42   A, no LH slur
43   E, RH 1 stacc., slur on last (instead of 1st) 3
          crotchets; cf. 124
49   A, RH slur 1–7, no stacc.
58   A, no stacc.
64–5   A, slur 1–9; E, slurs 1–8, 9–11, no tie
68   E, RH slur 3–5
79–80   E, RH slurs 79, 6 to 80, 1 and 80, ?2–4
83,89   A, RH slurs 1–5; E, ambiguous (see 39, also 1)
85,87   A, no RH slurs
86   A, no LH slur; E, LH slur 4–5, but cf. 42
88   A, no 2nd slur in RH
91,93   A, RH slur 1–6 only
92   A, no RH slur
95–9   A, no articulation; E, slurs over last 3 of 4-note
          groups in 96–7 (2nd), 98: cf. 104
101   A, no stacc.
101–12   A, no slurs (except RH, 107, and LH, 104, 106,
          108, 112) or stacc.
113,115   A, no stacc.
114   E, no LH slurs
121   A, RH slur 5–10
125   A, RH no 2nd slur
126–8   LH slurs, E 126, 127–8; A 126–end of system,
          probably 126–8 intended in 1 slur (cf. 39–47)
127   A, no articulation
131   E, RH slurs 1–3, 4–9
132–3   A, RH no articulation
138   E, no RH slur
139   A, no stacc.
140   A, RH only slur 5–6
142   A, RH only slur 1–2
143–69   this passage in E only
155–6   155, RH slur, ?4–6; 156, 1st RH slur 2 or 3–5
170–75   A, no RH slurs, 171, 175, no LH slurs, 170–73
173   A, RH slur ?begins on 5
174   E, RH slurs 2–5, 7–10
176   see 1
180   A and E, RH slur 1–5 only; cf. 39, 83 etc.
183   E, 1st RH slur 1–2 (probably because of confusion
          caused by LH notes in system above)
184–6   A, no stacc.

SONATA in F

K533 (1786-8)

Allegro

* The absence of an opening dynamic mark usually implies *f*. The recapitulation, however, is *p* (b.145). If the opening is played *p*,
  f is suggested at either b.9 or b.32

A.B. 1517

* Mozart's wedges above tied notes in this passage (also those later in the movement) denote accents, not staccato.

Andante

* the wedges denote accents rather than staccato, as in the first movement (see also bars 102, 104, 111 and the added analogous ones in 34, 36, 43).

* wedges in this passage denote accents, not staccato.

RONDO
Allegretto

ABRSM PUBLISHING

**The Associated Board of
the Royal Schools of Music
(Publishing) Limited**

14 Bedford Square
London WC1B 3JG

ISBN 1-85472-108-9

9 781854 721082